Time Pieces for Clarinet

Volume 1

for Clare, Philip and Josh

*c.*1565 When May is in his prime

attrib. Richard Edwards
(*c.*1523–1566)

*c.*1600 Wolsey's Wilde

William Byrd
(1543–1623)

AB 2674

1663 Duke of York's March

Anon.

c.1690 Menuet

Nicolas Lebègue
(1631–1702)

c.1700 Abigail Judge

Turlough O'Carolan
(1670–1738)

AB 2674

c.1740 Sarabande

BWV 833/4

Johann Sebastian Bach
(1685–1750)

Andante con moto (♩ = c.84)

c.1776 Sweet Kitty

Anon.
collected and arranged
by Cecil Sharp
(1859–1924)

Moderato (♩ = c.100)

1785 Minuet

Hob. IX/8 No. 12

Joseph Haydn
(1732–1809)

Tempo di minuetto (♩ = c.112–116)

1787 Die kleine Spinnerin

(The little spinner) K. 531

Wolfgang Amadeus Mozart
(1756–1791)

Quite lively (♩ = c.84–92)

c.1810 Rondo

Anton Diabelli
(1781–1858)

Allegro moderato (♩ = c.108)

AB 2674

1820 Ländler

D. 366 No. 6

Franz Schubert
(1797–1828)

Tempo di ländler (♩ = *c*.116–120)

1840 Air Français

Carl Czerny
(1791–1857)

Andante (♩ = *c*.76)

D.C. al Fine

1850 Heaving the Anchor

Traditional Russian

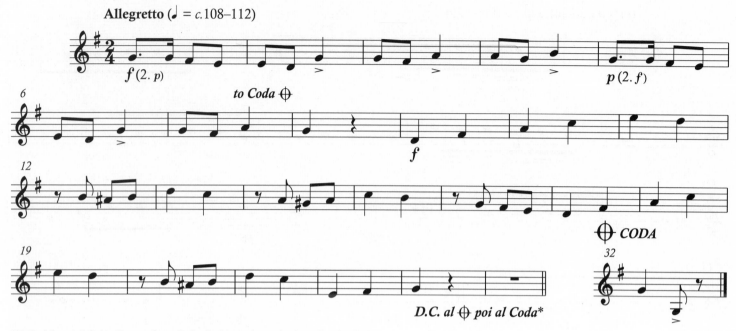

D.C. al ⊕ poi al Coda – Repeat from the beginning as far as ⊕, then play the Coda

1862 Allegro

Heinrich Wohlfahrt
(1797–1883)

1865 Waltz
Op. 39 No. 5

Johannes Brahms
(1833–1897)

Grazioso ($\quarternote$ = *c.*112)

*c.*1866 Dans les Ruines d'une Abbaye
(In the Ruins of an Abbey)
Op. 2 No. 1

Gabriel Fauré
(1845–1924)

Allegro ma non troppo ($\dottedquarternote$ = *c.*84)

AB 2674

1878 March of the Wooden Soldiers

from *Album for the Young*, Op. 39 No. 5

Pyotr Tchaikovsky
(1840–1893)

1890 Old Christmas Carol

from *L'Organiste*

César Franck
(1822–1890)

1902 Dedication

from *Stories of the Young*, Op. 1

Enrique Granados
(1867–1916)

1907 Song of Liberty

from *Pomp and Circumstance March No. 4*

Edward Elgar
(1857–1934)

1926 A Spring Morning

from *In The Country*, Op. 99

Alexander Grechaninov
(1864–1956)

1946 An Old Dance

from *30 Pieces for Children*, Op. 27 No. 7

Dmitri Kabalevsky
(1904–1987)

The mordents (∿) are optional.

AB 2674

1947 Children's Dance No. 1

Zoltán Kodály
(1882–1967)

Allegretto (♩ = c.72–76)

1952 Waltz

George Dyson
(1883–1964)

Tempo di valse (♩. = c.54)

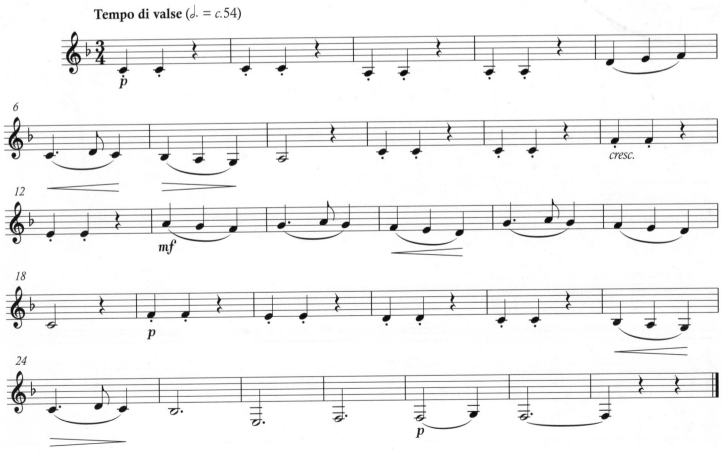

1952 A-B-C

from Reschofsky: *44 Kleine Klavierstücke von 9 Komponisten*

Leó Weiner
(1885–1960)

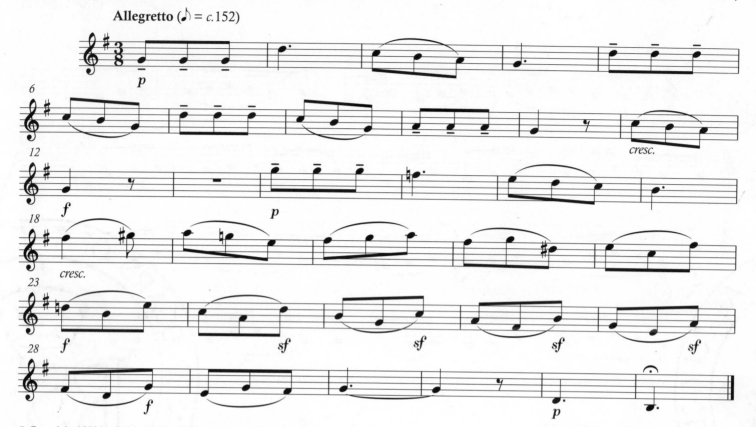

© Copyright 1952 by Editio Musica Budapest.

1992 Ronde

from *Images Enfantines*

Pierre Baubet-Gony
(1934–1997)

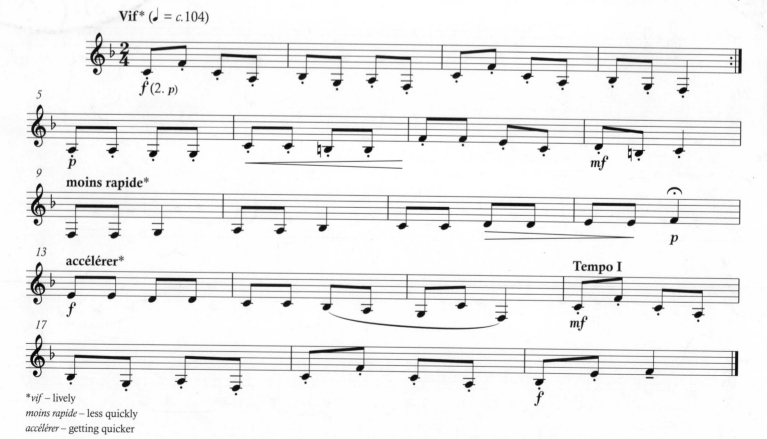

vif – lively

moins rapide – less quickly

accélérer – getting quicker

AB 2674

Music origination by
Barnes Music Engraving Ltd, East Sussex
Printed in England by Caligraving Ltd, Thetford, Norfolk

2:01

Time Pieces

for
Clarinet

Music through the Ages in 3 Volumes

Volume 1

**Selected and arranged by
Ian Denley**

**The Associated Board of
the Royal Schools of Music**

CONTENTS

Time Pieces for Clarinet

Volume 1

for Clare, Philip and Josh

c.1565 When May is in his prime

attrib. Richard Edwards
(*c.*1523–1566)

Vivace (♩ = *c.*144-160)

AB 2674

*c.*1600 Wolsey's Wilde

William Byrd
(1543–1623)

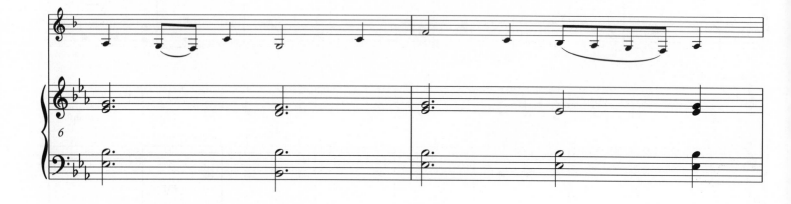

1663 Duke of York's March

Anon.

*c.*1690 **Menuet**

Nicolas Lebègue
(1631–1702)

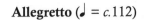

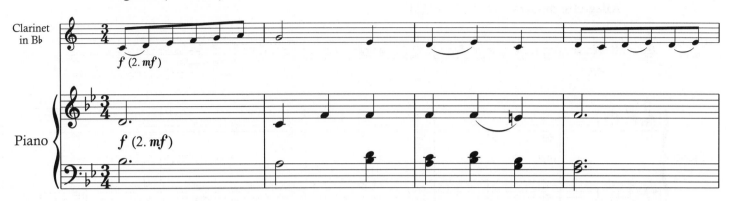

*c.*1700 Abigail Judge

Turlough O'Carolan
(1670–1738)

Allegretto moderato (♩ = *c.*112–116)

c.1740 Sarabande

BWV 833/4

Johann Sebastian Bach
(1685–1750)

Andante con moto (♩ = *c*.84)

poco rit.

*c.*1776 Sweet Kitty

Anon.
collected and arranged
by Cecil Sharp
(1859–1924)

AB 2674

1785 Minuet
Hob. IX/8 No. 12

Joseph Haydn
(1732–1809)

1787 Die kleine Spinnerin

(The little spinner) K. 531

Wolfgang Amadeus Mozart
(1756–1791)

Quite lively (♩ = c.84–92)

AB 2674

*c.*1810 Rondo

Anton Diabelli
(1781–1858)

1820 Ländler

D. 366 No. 6

Franz Schubert
(1797–1828)

Tempo di ländler (♩ = *c.*116–120)

AB 2674

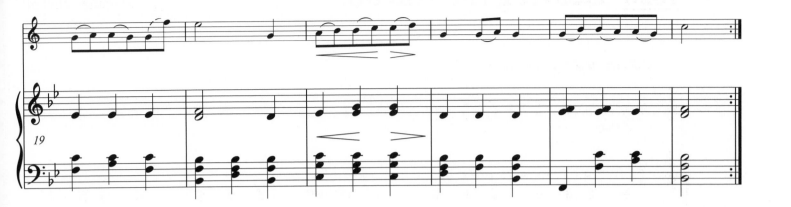

<u>1840</u> Air Français

Carl Czerny
(1791–1857)

Fine

D.C. al Fine

1850 Heaving the Anchor

Traditional Russian

D.C. al ⊕ poi al Coda – Repeat from the beginning as far as ⊕, then play the Coda

1862 Allegro

Heinrich Wohlfahrt
(1797–1883)

1865 Waltz
Op. 39 No. 5

Johannes Brahms
(1833–1897)

Grazioso (♩ = *c*.112)

c.1866 Dans les Ruines d'une Abbaye

(In the Ruins of an Abbey)

Op. 2 No. 1

Gabriel Fauré
(1845–1924)

Allegro ma non troppo (♩. = c.84)

Clarinet in B♭

Piano

1878 March of the Wooden Soldiers

from *Album for the Young*, Op. 39 No. 5

Pyotr Tchaikovsky
(1840–1893)

Moderato (♩ = *c.*116–120)

AB 2674

1890 Old Christmas Carol

from *L'Organiste*

César Franck
(1822–1890)

AB 2674

1902 Dedication

from *Stories of the Young*, Op. 1

Enrique Granados
(1867–1916)

1907 Song of Liberty

from *Pomp and Circumstance March No. 4*

Edward Elgar
(1857–1934)

Allegro marziale (♩ = *c.*108)

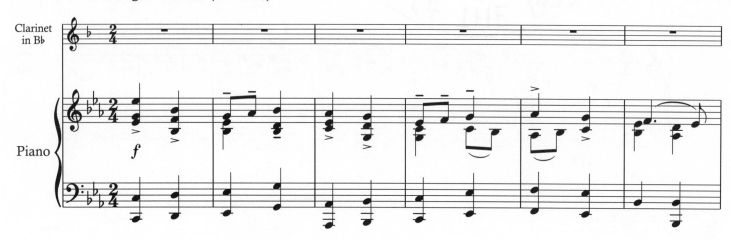

AB 2674

1926 A Spring Morning

from *In The Country*, Op. 99

Alexander Grechaninov
(1864–1956)

AB 2674

1946 An Old Dance

from *30 Pieces for Children*, Op. 27 No. 7

Dmitri Kabalevsky
(1904–1987)

The mordents (𝆮) are optional.

AB 2674

1947 Children's Dance No. 1

Zoltán Kodály
(1882–1967)

AB 2674

1952 Waltz

George Dyson
(1883–1964)

Tempo di valse ($\downarrow$. = *c*.54)

1952 A-B-C

from Reschofsky: *44 Kleine Klavierstücke von 9 Komponisten*

Leó Weiner
(1885–1960)

AB 2674

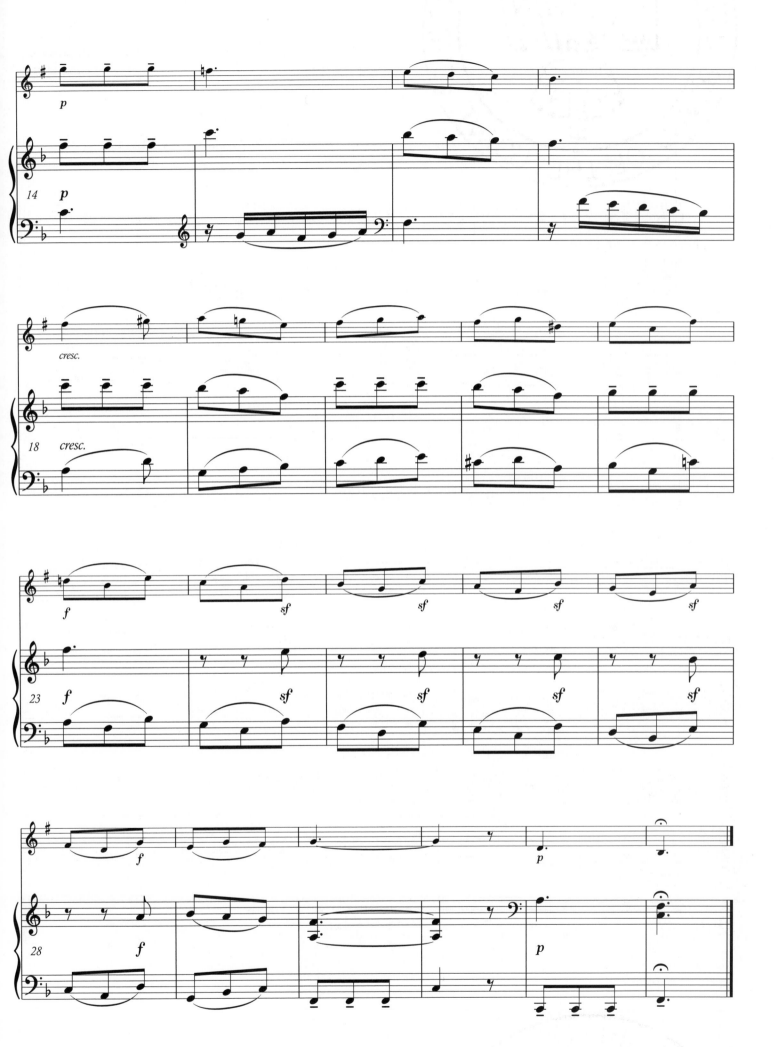

1992 Ronde

from *Images Enfantines*

Pierre Baubet-Gony
(1934–1997)

vif – lively

moins rapide – less quickly

accélérer – getting quicker

AB 2674

Music origination by
Barnes Music Engraving Ltd, East Sussex
Printed in England by Caligraving Ltd, Thetford, Norfolk